Dallas Cowboys Trivia Quiz Book

500 Questions on America's Team

Chris Bradshaw

D1468911

Every effort has been made by the author and publishing house to ensure that the information contained in this book was correct as of press time. The author and publishing house hereby disclaim and do not assume liability for any injury, loss, damage, or disruption caused by errors or omissions, regardless of whether any errors or omissions result from negligence, accident, or any other cause. Readers are encouraged to verify any information contained in this book prior to taking any action on the information.

For rights and permissions, please contact:

Chris Bradshaw

C_D_Bradshaw@hotmail.com

ISBN: 1725650835
ISBN-13: 978-172650831

Front cover image created by headfuzz by grimboid. Check out his great collection of TV, movie and sport-themed posters online at:

https://www.etsy.com/shop/headfuzzbygrimboid

Introduction

Think you know about the Dallas Cowboys? Put your knowledge to the test with this selection of quizzes on America's Team.

The book covers the whole history of the franchise, from the glory days under Tom Landry, the 1990s triumphs of Johnson and Switzer right up to the present day.

The biggest names in Cowboys history are present and correct so look out for questions on Troy Aikman, Emmitt Smith, Tony Romo, Dak Prescott, Tony Dorsett, Ezekiel Elliott, Michael Irvin and many, many more.

There are 500 questions in all covering running backs and receivers, coaches and quarterbacks, pass rushers and punters and much else besides.

Each quiz contains a selection of 20 questions and is either a mixed bag of pot luck testers or is centered on a specific category such as the 1990s or defense.

There are easy, medium and hard questions offering something for Dallas novices as well as connoisseurs of Cowboys history.

You'll find the answers to each quiz below the bottom of the following quiz. For example, the answers to Quiz 1: Pot Luck, are underneath Quiz 2: Quarterbacks. The only exception is Quiz 25: Pot Luck. The answers to these can be found under the Quiz 1 questions.

All statistics refer to the regular season only unless otherwise stated and are accurate up to the start of the 2018 season.

We hope you enjoy the Dallas Cowboys Trivia Quiz Book.

October 2021 Update

This latest edition of the Dallas Cowboys Trivia Quiz Book has been fully revised and updated. All statistics and records are now accurate to the start of the 2021 season.

You'll also find 100 brand-new trivia teasers to test your knowledge on America's Team. These are at the back of the book in the Bonus Questions section. As usual, you'll find the answers to each quiz at the bottom of the quiz that follows.

Good luck!

About the Author

Chris Bradshaw has written more than 30 quiz books including titles for Britain's biggest selling daily newspaper, The Sun, and The Times (London).

In addition to the NFL, he has written extensively on soccer, cricket, darts and poker.

He lives in Birmingham, England and has been following the NFL for over 30 years.

Acknowledgements

Many thanks to Ken and Veronica Bradshaw, Heidi Grant, Steph, James, Ben and Will Roe, Graham Nash and Geoff Callow.

CONTENTS

Quiz 1: Pot Luck

1. Which head coach steered the Cowboys to their first two Super Bowl triumphs?

2. What colors are the stripes on the Cowboys helmet?

3. Whom did Jason Garrett succeed as the Cowboys head coach?

4. Which Cowboy was the first player in NFL history to rush for over 100 yards in each of the first eight games of a season?

5. In 1991, which Dallas running back and receiver became the first pair of players from the same team to lead the NFL in rushing and receiving yards in the same year?

6. Who holds the franchise record for the most games played?

7. Whose 83-yard touchdown reception against the Steelers in November 2016 is the longest in franchise history by a rookie?

8. Which opponent have the Cowboys beaten the most times in franchise history?

9. In what year did the Cowboys play their first game?

10. What is the name of the Cowboys mascot?

11. In 1989, the Cowboys traded which offensive star for five players and six draft picks?

12. Which team was on the other side of that historic trade?

13. Which quarterback also served as the team's punter during the late 1970s and early 1980s?

14. Which Dallas offensive lineman went to the Pro Bowl 10 times between 1995 and 2005?

15. Who was the only Cowboy to win the NFL Man of the Year Award in the 1990s?

16. 'Too Tall' was the nickname of which defensive superstar?

17. Which former Cowboy is the only man to have played in both the Super Bowl and baseball's World Series?

18. Which two Cowboys head coaches also won the national college championship?

19. In what round of the NFL Draft did the Cowboys select running back Herschel Walker? a) first b) third c) fifth

20. Under Tom Landry's leadership the Cowboys enjoyed how many consecutive winning seasons? a) 18 b) 19 c) 20

Quiz 25: Answers

1. Michael Irvin 2. Chuck Howley and Larry Brown 3. Ebenezer Ekuban 4. Mel Renfro 5. Bill Bates 6. True 7. Punt 8. Miami 9. False 10. Winning 11. Louis-Philippe 12. Cowboys Stadium 13. True 14. Jimmy Johnson 15. Atlanta 16. Charlie Waters 17. 'Living The American Dream' 18. Darren Woodson 19. a) 176 passes 20. a) Tom Brady

Quiz 2: Quarterbacks

1. Who is the Cowboys' all-time leader in passing yards?

2. Who led the team in passing for 12 straight years between 1989 and 2000?

3. In which round of the 2016 NFL Draft did the Cowboys select Dak Prescott?

4. Tony Romo threw for a franchise record 506 yards but still ended up on the losing side in a 2013 game against which AFC team?

5. Who holds the team record for the most passing yards by a rookie quarterback?

6. Who holds the record for the most passing attempts in team history?

7. The longest pass in team history was a 95-yard touchdown against Washington in 1966 thrown by which quarterback?

8. Who is the unlikely holder of the franchise record for the most consecutive pass completions with 21?

9. Tony Romo holds the record for the most touchdown passes by a Dallas quarterback. Who is second on that list?

10. Which former New England quarterback spent the final two years of his NFL career with the Cowboys amassing a 12-10 starting record in 2005 and 2006?

11. Dak Prescott played college ball at which southern school?

12. Who tied a franchise record in 1980 after throwing 25 interceptions?

13. True or false – Tony Romo is the only Dallas quarterback to throw over 30 touchdown passes in a single season?

14. Which veteran quarterback, best known for his time in Philadelphia, threw six touchdown passes in his only season in Dallas in 2000?

15. Who led the Cowboys to a 10-6 record and a playoff berth in 2003 but was released before the start of the 2004 season?

16. Who threw for more yards while with the Cowboys – Roger Staubach or Danny White?

17. The Cowboys have used a first round draft pick to select a quarterback just twice in franchise history. Who were the two quarterbacks selected?

18. Of Dallas quarterbacks with over 1,500 attempts who has the best completion percentage?

19. In 1999, Troy Aikman attempted how many consecutive passes without throwing a pick? a) 216 b) 226 c) 236

20. How many regular season touchdown passes did Tony Romo throw in his career? a) 248 b) 258 c) 268

Quiz 1: Answers

1. Tom Landry 2. White and blue 3. Wade Phillips 4. DeMarco Murray 5. Emmitt Smith and Michael Irvin 6. Jason Witten 7. Ezekiel Elliott 8. Washington 9. 1960 10. Rowdy 11. Herschel Walker 12. Minnesota 13. Danny White 14. Larry Allen 15. Troy Aikman 16. Ed Jones 17. Deion Sanders 18. Jimmy Johnson and Barry Switzer 19. c) Fifth 20. c) 20

Quiz 3: Pot Luck

1. Long-time Cowboy Jason Witten is second on the list of most receptions by a tight end in NFL history. Who tops that list?

2. 'Moose' was the nickname of which popular Cowboy?

3. In 1980, who became the first Cowboy to enter the Pro Football Hall of Fame?

4. Throughout his career Emmitt Smith rushed for more yards (2,746) against which team than any other?

5. What color jerseys do the Cowboys usually wear in home games?

6. Which alliteratively named safety played in 217 games for the Cowboys between 1983 and 1997?

7. The Cowboys have suffered more regular season losses to which opponent than any other?

8. On 28 September 1975 the Cowboys beat St. Louis 37-31. What was unique about this game?

9. Which third-string quarterback steered the Cowboys to an unlikely 42-31 Thanksgiving Day victory over Green Bay in 1994?

10. Which defensive lineman famously fumbled after being chased down by receiver Don Beebe in Super Bowl XXVII?

11. Which Boise State linebacker did the Cowboys select with their first pick in the 2018 NFL Draft?

12. Who is the only Cowboys offensive player to have been voted to the Pro Bowl 11 times?

13. Up to and including the 2021 season, the Cowboys had had how many head coaches throughout the history of the franchise?

14. Part of the Cowboys' 2021 training camp was held at Oxnard which is in which state?

15. Who served as the Cowboys president and general manager for 29 years until 1989?

16. How many regular season rushing touchdowns did Troy Aikman score in his NFL career?

17. Deion Sanders joined the Cowboys as a free agent after he left which team?

18. During the 2020 season, the Cowboys played a game on what day of the week for the first time in their history?

19. The Cowboys set the record for the largest regular season attendance in NFL history in a 2009 game against which team? a) New York Giants b) Philadelphia c) Washington

20. What was the crowd at that record-breaking game? a) 103,121 b) 104,121 c) 105,121

Quiz 2: Answers

1. Tony Romo 2. Troy Aikman 3. Fourth 4. Denver 5. Dak Prescott 6. Troy Aikman 7. Don Meredith 8. Brandon Weedon 9. Troy Aikman 10. Drew Bledsoe 11. Mississippi State 12. Danny White 13. True 14. Randall Cunningham 15. Quincy Carter 16. Roger Staubach 17. Craig Morton and Troy Aikman 18. Dak Prescott 19. a) 216 20. a) 248

Quiz 4: Running Backs

1. Who is the Cowboys' all-time leading rusher?

2. With which pick of the 2016 NFL Draft did the Cowboys select Ezekiel Elliott?

3. The longest rush in team history was a 99-yard touchdown run by which back?

4. Before Ezekiel Elliott, who was the last running back selected by the Cowboys in the first round of the NFL Draft?

5. Who holds the franchise record for the most rushing yards in a season?

6. Who are the three Cowboys backs to have won the NFL rushing title?

7. Which former fourth overall pick for the Raiders led the Cowboys in rushing in 2015 after racking up 1,089 yards?

8. Who holds the team record for the most 100-yard rushing games in a single season?

9. How many times did he break the century mark to set that record?

10. True or false – In a 2007 game against Washington the Cowboys gained just one rushing yard?

11. Who are the two Cowboys to rush for over 1,000 yards in their rookie season?

12. Whose 73-yard touchdown run against Philadelphia in January 2010 is the longest by a Dallas back in playoff games?

13. DeMarco Murray rushed for a team record 253 yards in a 2011 game against which NFC West team?

14. Who are the two Dallas backs with over 1,000 rushing yards in playoff games?

15. Ezekiel Elliott played college ball at which school?

16. Emmitt Smith holds the record for the most touchdowns in a single season. How many times did he score in 1995?

17. Which rookie rushed for 198 yards in a December 2004 game in Seattle?

18. Who rushed for more regular season yards while with the Cowboys – Marion Barber or DeMarco Murray?

19. Between 1993 and 1996 Emmitt Smith rushed for a touchdown in how many consecutive playoff games? a) six b) seven c) eight

20. What is the most rushing yards gained by a Cowboys back in a single season? a) 1,713 b) 1,773 c) 1,845

Quiz 3: Answers

1. Tony Gonzalez 2. Daryl Johnston 3. Bob Lilly 4. Philadelphia 5. White 6. Bill Bates 7. Philadelphia 8. It was the team's first overtime win 9. Jason Garrett 10. Leon Lett 11. Leighton Vander Esch 12. Jason Witten 13. Nine 14. California 15. Tex Schramm 16. Nine 17. San Francisco 18. Tuesday 19. a) New York Giants 20. a) 105,121

Quiz 5: Pot Luck

1. Who is the Cowboys' all-time leader in receptions?

2. The Cowboys claimed their first Super Bowl victory wearing what color jerseys?

3. Which Cowboys quarterback's 104.9 passers rating is the best in NFL history by a rookie?

4. What color is the star on the Cowboys helmet?

5. Despite being drafted in 1964, quarterback Roger Staubach didn't play for the Cowboys until 1969 due to his commitments with which branch of the military?

6. Which quarterback has thrown the most touchdown passes for the Cowboys in playoff games?

7. Who is the only Dallas defensive player to be voted to the Pro Bowl 11 times?

8. Who are the three Dallas quarterbacks to throw for over 300 yards in a playoff game?

9. Immediately prior to becoming head coach of the Cowboys Jimmy Johnson had been the head coach at which college?

10. Do the Cowboys have a winning or losing record in games played on Thanksgiving Day?

11. Which defensive tackle, who won the World Bowl in 1997 with the Barcelona Dragons, went to the Pro Bowl in each of his four seasons with the Cowboys between 2002 and 2005?

12. After 13 years in Dallas Emmitt Smith spent the final two years of his NFL career with which team?

13. Who is the only Cowboys quarterback to throw 20 touchdown passes in his rookie season?

14. Which Cowboys executive was inducted into the Pro Football Hall of Fame in 2017?

15. 'The Manster' was the nickname of which Hall of Fame defender?

16. Which current NFL team have the Cowboys beaten the fewest times in franchise history?

17. Who was the only Cowboy to play under both Jimmy Johnson and Bill Parcells?

18. What first was created when the Cowboys played the Oilers in Houston on 24 November 1974?

19. What is DeMarcus Lawrence's nickname? a) Jeep b) Jet c) Tank

20. What is the most points scored by the Cowboys in a single regular season? a) 469 b) 479 c) 489

Quiz 4: Answers

1. Emmitt Smith 2. Fourth 3. Tony Dorsett 4. Felix Jones 5. DeMarco Murray 6. Emmitt Smith, DeMarco Murray and Ezekiel Elliott 7. Darren McFadden 8. DeMarco Murray 9. Twelve 10. True 11. Tony Dorsett and Ezekiel Elliott 12. Felix Jones 13. Arizona 14. Emmitt Smith and Tony Dorsett 15. Ohio State 16. 25 times 17. Julius Jones 18. DeMarco Murray 19. c) Eight 20. c) 1,845

Quiz 6: Receivers

1. Who are the two Cowboys with over 10,000 receiving yards?

2. Who set the record for the most receiving yards in a game after amassing 250 against the Chiefs in 2009?

3. Who holds the franchise record for the most regular season touchdown catches with 73?

4. Before Jason Witten, who was the last tight end to lead the Cowboys in the most receptions in a season? (clue: it was 1984)

5. Which versatile running back led the team in receptions in both 1986 and 1987?

6. Michael Irvin is one of just two Cowboys receivers with over 1,000 receiving yards in playoff games. Who is the other?

7. Who holds the record for the most receptions in a single regular season with 111?

8. Which receiver caught 24 passes for 655 yards and a mammoth 27.3 yards per catch average in playoff games between 1991 and 1994?

9. Who holds the team record for the most touchdown catches by a Cowboys tight end in playoff games?

10. Of Cowboys receivers with over 200 receptions who has the best yards per catch average?

11. True or false – No Cowboy has caught over 50 passes in their rookie season?

12. Who holds the record for the most touchdown receptions in a single season with 16?

13. Who led the team in receiving yards every year between 1978 and 1985?

14. In February 2000, the Cowboys traded two first round draft picks to Seattle to acquire which receiver?

15. Before Dez Bryant in 2010, who was the last wide receiver selected by the Cowboys in the first round of the NFL Draft? (clue: it was 1991)

16. Which Dallas receiver caught six passes for a rookie record 203 yards against the Cardinals in November 1989?

17. Who is the only Cowboy to record over 1,000 receiving yards in his rookie year?

18. Which controversial receiver tied a franchise record after catching four touchdown passes against Washington in November 2007?

19. Michael Irvin was one of just two Cowboys with a 1,000-receiving yard season in the 1990s. Who was the other? a) Rocket Ismail b) Kelvin Martin c) Keyshawn Johnson

20. Michael Irvin holds the team record for the most receiving yards in a single season. How many did he amass in 1995? a) 1,503 b) 1,603 c) 1,703

Quiz 5: Answers

1. Jason Witten 2. White 3. Dak Prescott 4. Blue with white edging 5. The Navy 6. Roger Staubach with 24 7. Bob Lilly 8. Troy Aikman, Danny White and Dak Prescott 9. University of Miami 10. Winning 11. La'Roi Glover 12. Arizona 13. Dak Prescott 14. Jerry Jones 15. Randy White 16. Baltimore Ravens 17. Darren Woodson 18. It was their first ever game in a dome 19. c) Tank 20. b) 479

Quiz 7: Pot Luck

1. Do the Cowboys have an overall winning or losing record in playoff games?

2. Which three Cowboys greats were known collectively as 'The Triplets'?

3. What color jerseys did the Cowboys wear on their unsuccessful trip to Super Bowl V?

4. 'Mr Cowboy' was the nickname of which defensive star?

5. Which quarterback / wide receiver tandem have combined for the most touchdowns in team history?

6. Which running back's 91-yard touchdown reception versus Baltimore in 1978 is the second longest in team history?

7. Who holds the record for the most consecutive games played in team history?

8. What number jersey did star quarterback Troy Aikman wear?

9. True or false – In a 1980 game against Baltimore the Cowboys rushed for 354 yards?

10. Which cornerback, who spent four seasons in Dallas in the 2000s, later went on to become an NFL game official?

11. The Cowboys are the joint holders of the record for the most consecutive postseason appearances after reaching the playoffs how many seasons in a row?

12. Which former Dallas head coach is a regular Tweeter who uses the moniker @SonOfBum?

13. True or false – The Cowboys have never faced the New York Giants in the playoffs?

14. Whose 192 receiving yards against the 49ers in January 1995 are the most by a Dallas receiver in a playoff game?

15. Which Dallas defender was named the 2007 NFL Comeback Player of the Year?

16. DeMarcus Lawrence played college ball at which school?

17. Which team did the Cowboys defeat 21-7 to record their first ever win at AT&T Stadium?

18. Between 1988 and 1989 the Cowboys lost how many straight home games?

19. The first touchdown pass caught by Jason Witten was thrown by which quarterback? a) Quincy Carter b) Tony Romo c) Vinny Testaverde

20. What is the most touchdowns scored by the Cowboys in a single regular season? a) 56 b) 58 c) 60

Quiz 6: Answers

1. Jason Witten and Michael Irvin 2. Miles Austin 3. Dez Bryant 4. Doug Cosbie 5. Herschel Walker 6. Drew Pearson 7. Michael Irvin 8. Alvin Harper 9. Jay Novacek 10. Bob Hayes 11. False 12. Dez Bryant 13. Tony Hill 14. Joey Galloway 15. Alvin Harper 16. James Dixon 17. Bob Hayes 18. Terrell Owens 19. a) Rocket Ismail 20. b) 1,603

Quiz 8: Defense

1. Who is the Cowboys' all-time leader in sacks?

2. Which Cowboys linebacker set a team record after recording 22 tackles in a 2016 game against the Giants?

3. Which Cowboy is the only safety to have been named the Super Bowl MVP?

4. The Cowboys used the first overall pick of the 1991 NFL Draft to select which defensive lineman?

5. Which Dallas defensive back led the NFL in interceptions in both 1981 and 1982?

6. Which alliteratively named defensive end tied a franchise record after recording five sacks against Washington in November 1985?

7. Who is the team's all-time leader in interceptions, picking off 52 passes between 1964 and 1977?

8. Who holds the franchise record for the most sacks in a single season?

9. How many sacks did he record to set that record?

10. Who holds the franchise record for the most games played by a defensive player?

11. Which defensive tackle recorded a hat-trick of sacks in a January 1993 playoff game against the 49ers?

12. Who was the first player in NFL history to win five Super Bowl rings, winning two with San Francisco then three more with Dallas?

13. Which safety, who played between 1992 and 2003, is the team's all-time leader in tackles?

14. True or false – The Cowboys have never recorded a shutout in a playoff game?

15. Which linebacker tied a franchise record after returning four interceptions for touchdowns between 1997 and 2002?

16. Who are the two Dallas defenders to receive First-Team All-Pro honors seven times?

17. Who led the team in interceptions in 2003, 2004, 2008, 2010 and 2011?

18. Who returned a pick for a franchise record 101-yard touchdown against the Giants in November 2010?

19. What was the nickname of the dominant Dallas defense of the 1970s? a) All Star Defense b) Doomsday Defense c) Killer D Defense

20. What is the highest number of sacks the Cowboys defense has recorded in a single season? a) 58 b) 60 c) 62

Quiz 7: Answers

1. Winning 2. Troy Aikman, Michael Irvin and Emmitt Smith 3. Blue 4. Bob Lilly 5. Tony Romo to Dez Bryant 6. Tony Dorsett 7. L.P. Ladouceur 8. #8 9. True 10. Nate Jones 11. Nine 12. Wade Phillips 13. False 14. Michael Irvin 15. Greg Ellis 16. Boise State 17. Carolina 18. 14 games 19. a) Quincy Carter 20. c) 60

Quiz 9: Pot Luck

1. Who is the Cowboys' all-time leading scorer in playoff games?

2. The first player selected by the Cowboys in the NFL Draft went on to have a Hall of Fame career. Who was that defensive star?

3. Which running back was the last non-kicker to lead the Cowboys in points scored in a season?

4. During his illustrious career Larry Allen played every position on the offensive line bar one. Which one?

5. Which opposition receiver caught 14 passes for a mammoth 329 yards against the Cowboys in October 2013?

6. Up to the start of the 2021 season only one team had reached the Super Bowl more often than the Cowboys. Which one?

7. In each of his three seasons as head coach of the Cowboys Dave Campo had the same win loss record. What was it?

8. The Cowboys home jersey features how many blue stripes on each sleeve?

9. True or false – The Cowboys played in front of a crowd of less than 5,000 in a 1961 regular season game in Minnesota?

10. 'The Kitchen' was the nickname of which long-time Dallas o-lineman?

11. Excluding teams not currently in the NFC East which franchise have the Cowboys defeated the most times in their history?

12. Which Cowboy is the only man to have won a Super Bowl ring and an Olympic gold medal?

13. True or false – No Dallas quarterback has ever received First-Team All-Pro honors?

14. Which team defeated the Cowboys 27-26 on Christmas Day 2010?

15. Who was the only Cowboy to win the NFL Man of the Year Award in the 1970s?

16. True or false – Texas Stadium hosted games at the 1994 FIFA World Cup?

17. Up to the start of the 2021 season the Cowboys were unbeaten in playoff games against which three NFC teams?

18. What number jersey does quarterback Dak Prescott wear?

19. In the last week of the 1993 regular season Emmitt Smith rushed for 168 yards despite suffering from what injury? a) groin strain b) pulled hamstring c) separated shoulder

20. What is the most points that the Cowboys have given up in a single season? a) 453 b) 463 c) 473

Quiz 8: Answers

1. DeMarcus Ware 2. Sean Lee 3. Larry Brown 4. Russell Maryland 5. Everson Walls 6. Jim Jeffcoat 7. Mel Renfro 8. Harvey Martin 9. 23 sacks 10. Ed Jones 11. Tony Casillas 12. Charles Haley 13. Darren Woodson 14. False 15. Dexter Coakley 16. Bob Lilly and Randy White 17. Terence Newman 18. Bryan McCann 19. a) Doomsday Defense 20. c) 62

Quiz 10: Special Teams

1. Who holds the record for the converting the most field goals in team history?

2. Who returned a kickoff for a 93-yard touchdown against Seattle in January 2007?

3. Who is the only Dallas player to record four punt return touchdowns?

4. Long-time Dallas kicker Rafael Septien was born in which country?

5. Which kicker went a perfect seven for seven on field goals against Green Bay in November 1996?

6. Which rookie wide receiver returned two punts for touchdowns in 2010?

7. Since 2000, who are the two Dallas kickers to have been voted to the Pro Bowl?

8. Which kicker led the team in scoring for nine straight seasons between 1978 and 1986?

9. Of Dallas punters with over 300 attempts, who has the best average?

10. Which two-time winner of the NFL's 'Fastest Man' contest holds the record for the longest kick return in franchise history?

11. Which speedy wide receiver returned three punts and one kickoff for touchdowns in 1993 and 1994?

12. True or false – In 2015, punter Chris Jones failed to record a single touchback?

13. Whose 612 punts during the 1970s and 80s are the most in team history?

14. Which cornerback returned a punt 97 yards for a touchdown against the Lions in November 2010?

15. Which Cowboys long snapper was voted to the 2014 Pro Bowl?

16. Which kicker, who shares his name with a famous sitcom character, converted 75 field goals between 1997 and 1999?

17. Which kicker tied a franchise record against the Giants in 2003 after converting seven field goals?

18. Of Cowboys players with at least 75 punt returns, who has the best average?

19. What is the longest successful field goal in team history? a) 61 yards b) 62 yards c) 63 yards

20. Between 2013 and 2014 Dan Bailey successfully converted how many consecutive field goals? a) 28 b) 29 c) 30

Quiz 9: Answers

1. Emmitt Smith 2. Bob Lilly 3. Marion Barber 4. Center 5. Calvin Johnson 6. New England 7. 5 wins 11 losses 8. Two 9. True 10. Nate Newton 11. The Cardinals 12. Bob Hayes 13. True 14. Arizona 15. Roger Staubach 16. False 17. Atlanta, Chicago and Tampa Bay 18. #4 19. c) Separated shoulder 20. c) 473

Quiz 11: Pot Luck

1. 'Prime Time' was the nickname of which Cowboys defender?

2. Which Cowboys defensive star was 6-0 in his brief heavyweight boxing career in 1979 and 1980?

3. Which Cowboy was the first player in NFL history to rush for over 1,400 yards in four straight seasons?

4. For the first 11 years of their history the Cowboys called which stadium home?

5. Who are the three Dallas head coaches to have been born in Texas?

6. Between 1992 and 1995 the Cowboys beat which opponent in seven successive games?

7. Which defender appeared in 196 consecutive games between 1961 and 1974?

8. True or false – The Cowboys haven't been involved in a tied game since the 1960s?

9. Which famous nickname was coined by NFL Films' Bob Ryan?

10. In Troy Aikman's first 15 starts, how many games did the Cowboys win?

11. 'Big Tuna' was the nickname of which Cowboys head coach?

12. What number jersey did Hall of Fame running back Tony Dorsett wear?

13. True or false – The Cowboys have played on Thanksgiving Day every year since 1966?

14. What number jersey did quarterback Roger Staubach wear?

15. Who holds the franchise record after catching passes in 130 consecutive games?

16. Which long-time Cowboys quarterback later won two Arena League titles as head coach of the Arizona Rattlers?

17. Did Troy Aikman throw more or fewer than 10 pick sixes in his regular season career?

18. In which round of the 2014 NFL Draft did the Cowboys select star defensive lineman DeMarcus Lawrence?

19. What was the nickname of the dominant 1990s offensive line? a) The Great Wall of Dallas b) The Conquering Cowboys c) The Dallas Dam

20. The Cowboys won how many division titles under Tom Landry? a) 12 b) 13 c) 14

Quiz 10: Answers

1. Dan Bailey 2. Miles Austin 3. Deion Sanders 4. Mexico 5. Chris Boniol 6. Dez Bryant 7. Dan Bailey and Nick Folk 8. Rafael Septien 9. Mat McBriar 10. Alexander Wright 11. Kevin Williams 12. False (he had one) 13. Danny White 14. Bryan McCann 15. L.P. Ladouceur 16. Richie Cunningham 17. Billy Cundiff 18. Deion Sanders 19. c) 63 yards 20. c) 30

Quiz 12: 1970s

1. The 1970 Cowboys lost in Super Bowl V to which team?

2. The Cowboys won their first Super Bowl a year later, defeating which team in Super Bowl VI?

3. What was the score in that game?

4. Which future Super Bowl-winning head coach caught a touchdown pass for Dallas in Super Bowl VI?

5. Who was named the MVP of Super Bowl VI?

6. What venue hosted Super Bowl VI?

7. The 1975 Cowboys reached Super Bowl X, losing 21-17 to which team?

8. The 1977 Cowboys sealed their second World Championship, defeating which team in Super Bowl XII?

9. What was the score in that game?

10. Which duo were named co-MVPs at Super Bowl XII?

11. Which stadium played host to Super Bowl XII?

12. The 1978 Cowboys secured their fifth NFC title after defeating which team 28-0 in the Championship game?

13. Which team did the Cowboys then face in Super Bowl XIII?

14. What was the score in that epic encounter?

15. Which future Hall of Famer did Dallas choose with the second overall pick of the 1977 NFL Draft?

16. True or false – In Super Bowl XII the Cowboys held their opponents to just 35 passing yards?

17. Which defensive star did the Cowboys select with the first overall pick of the 1974 NFL Draft?

18. In 1972, who became the first Dallas back to rush for 1,000 yards in a single season?

19. How many losing seasons did the Cowboys have during the 1970s? a) zero b) one c) two

20. How many division titles did the Cowboys win during the 1970s? a) five b) six c) seven

Quiz 11: Answers

1. Deion Sanders 2. Ed 'Too Tall' Jones 3. Emmitt Smith 4. The Cotton Bowl 5. Tom Landry, Jimmy Johnson and Wade Phillips 6. Philadelphia 7. Bob Lilly 8. True 9. America's Team 10. One 11. Bill Parcells 12. #33 13. False 14. #12 15. Jason Witten 16. Danny White 17. More 18. Second 19. a) The Great Wall of Dallas 20. b) 13

Quiz 13: Pot Luck

1. Who is the only Cowboy to have won the Associated Press NFL MVP Award?

2. Which former Cowboys defensive lineman later entered the ring and took part in WWE's Wrestlemania 2?

3. Tony Romo's first touchdown pass was caught by which receiver?

4. In what year did the Cowboys play their first game at Texas Stadium?

5. Which Dallas quarterback was nicknamed 'Captain Comeback'?

6. Excluding Tom Landry, which head coach has steered the Cowboys to the most regular season wins?

7. Tony Romo played college ball at which school?

8. How many games did the Cowboys win in their first NFL season?

9. Which future Jaguars and Raiders head coach led the Cowboys in tackles in 1991?

10. Which Cowboys head coach is credited with creating the so-called 'Flex Defense'?

11. True or false – The Cowboys were unbeaten in the 16 games in which Calvin Hill rushed for 100 yards or more?

12. In the 1975 Divisional Round playoff Roger Staubach completed a last-minute 'Hail Mary' to which receiver to give the Cowboys an amazing win?

13. Which team did the Cowboys defeat thanks to that historic 'Hail Mary'?

14. Who are the three Cowboys coaches to have won the AP NFL Coach of the Year Award?

15. Who is the only player in Cowboys history to have worn the #74 jersey?

16. Before becoming head coach in Dallas Tom Landry had spent six years as defensive coordinator of which team?

17. Who are the two Dallas quarterbacks to have been voted to the Pro Bowl six times?

18. Which Cowboys great made a cameo appearance in the hit TV comedy 'How I Met Your Mother'?

19. What was the nickname of Hall of Fame lineman Rayfield Wright? a) Big Bird b) Big Cat c) Big Dog

20. Kicker Toni Fritsch was born in which country? a) Austria b) The Netherlands c) Sweden

Quiz 12: Answers

1. Baltimore 2. Miami 3. Cowboys 24-3 Dolphins 4. Mike Ditka 5. Roger Staubach 6. Tulane Stadium 7. Pittsburgh 8. Denver 9. Cowboys 27-10 Broncos 10. Randy White and Harvey Martin 11. Louisiana Superdome 12. Los Angeles Rams 13. Pittsburgh 14. Steelers 35-31 Cowboys 15. Tony Dorsett 16. True 17. Ed 'Too Tall' Jones 18. Calvin Hill 19. a) Zero 20. c) Seven

Quiz 14: 1980s

1. In October 1980, the Cowboys tied a franchise record after scoring 59 points against which NFC West team?

2. The Cowboys were beaten 20-7 by which divisional rival in the 1980 NFC Championship game?

3. The 1981 Cowboys routed which team 38-0 in the Divisional round of the playoffs?

4. The 1981 team just missed out on the Super Bowl once again, losing 28-27 to which team in the NFC title game?

5. Who was the only Dallas quarterback elected to the Pro Bowl in the 1980s?

6. In 1985, which Cowboy became only the sixth player in NFL history to rush for over 10,000 yards?

7. In November 1985, the Cowboys suffered their biggest ever defeat, losing 44-0 to which team?

8. In 1988, the Cowboys suffered one of their worst ever defeats, losing 43-3 to which then NFC Central team?

9. In January 1986, the Cowboys suffered their first and so far, only playoff shutout. Which team beat them 20-0?

10. What did the Cowboys do in 1986 that they hadn't previously done since 1964?

11. Which wide receiver did the Cowboys pick in the first round of the 1988 NFL Draft?

12. How many games did the Cowboys win in Tom Landry's final season as head coach?

13. In 1988, the Cowboys lost how many games on the bounce?

14. Who was the only Cowboys receiver to record a 1,000-yard season during the 1980s?

15. Which alliteratively named kicker converted four field goals in a quarter against the Giants in 1987?

16. Who were the three Dallas backs to lead the team in rushing during the 1980s?

17. Who was the Cowboys head coach at the end of the 1980s?

18. Who did the Cowboys select with the first overall pick the 1989 NFL Draft?

19. How many division titles did the Cowboys win during the 1980s? a) One b) Two c) Three

20. The anemic 1989 Cowboys were the least prolific in team history. How many points did they score? a) 206 b) 216 c) 226

Quiz 13: Answers

1. Emmitt Smith 2. Harvey Martin 3. Terrell Owens 4. 1971 5. Roger Staubach 6. Jason Garrett 7. Eastern Illinois 8. None 9. Jack Del Rio 10. Tom Landry 11. False 12. Drew Pearson 13. Minnesota 14. Tom Landry, Jimmy Johnson and Jason Garrett 15. Bob Lilly 16. New York Giants 17. Roger Staubach and Troy Aikman 18. Emmitt Smith 19. b) Big Cat 20. a) Austria

Quiz 15: Pot Luck

1. Before Dak Prescott who was the last rookie quarterback to start for the Cowboys?

2. 'The Barbarian' was the nickname of which hard-running Cowboys back?

3. Which Cowboys head coach has the best regular season winning percentage?

4. Up to the close of the 2020 season the Cowboys had played in the Super Bowl how many times?

5. Which former Cowboys quarterback later went on to play Detective Bert Jameson in the long-running drama 'Police Story'?

6. Which Dallas defensive coordinator was fired in January 2021?

7. True or false – No Cowboy has returned a punt for a touchdown in a playoff game?

8. Which Hall of Famer, who played for Dallas between 1967 and 1979, made appearances at tight end and defensive end before settling into his regular role as offensive tackle?

9. Which quarterback has been sacked the most times in team history?

10. True or false – Throughout his entire career Charles Haley never played on a team that finished a season with a losing record?

11. Former defensive coordinator Rod Marinelli spent three seasons as the head coach of which NFC team?

12. Which undrafted free agent caught 301 passes for 4,481 yards in eight seasons with the Cowboys between 2006 and 2013?

13. Who are the three Heisman Trophy winners to have been drafted by the Cowboys?

14. Up to and including the 2021 NFL Draft, the Cowboys had drafted more players from which two colleges than any other?

15. Jason Witten wore what number jersey?

16. Who sacked Miami quarterback Bob Griese for a record 29-yard loss in Super Bowl VI?

17. Which full back threw a 29-yard touchdown pass in Super Bowl XII?

18. Which tough receiver missed just one game despite breaking his jaw in a 2003 game against Arizona?

19. Approximately how much did Jerry Jones pay to purchase the Cowboys franchise? a) $140m b) $240m c) $340m

20. Including the playoffs, how many games did the Cowboys win with Tom Landry as head coach? a) 250 b) 260 c) 270

Quiz 14: Answers

1. San Francisco 2. Philadelphia 3. Tampa Bay 4. San Francisco 5. Danny White 6. Tony Dorsett 7. Chicago 8. Minnesota 9. L.A. Rams 10. Record a losing season 11. Michael Irvin 12. Three 13. Ten 14. Tony Hill 15. Roger Ruzek 16. Tony Dorsett, Herschel Walker and Paul Palmer 17. Jimmy Johnson 18. Troy Aikman 19. b) Two 20. a) 206

Quiz 16: 1990s

1. Which team did the Cowboys face in Super Bowl XXVII?

2. What was the score in that game?

3. Who was named the game's Most Valuable Player?

4. Which famous stadium hosted Super Bowl XXVII?

5. Which two Dallas defenders scored touchdowns in Super Bowl XXVII?

6. The 1993 Cowboys retained their Super Bowl crown, defeating which team 30-13?

7. Who scored two touchdowns en route to the MVP award in Super Bowl XXVIII?

8. Which defensive back returned a fumble 46 yards for a score in Super Bowl XXVIII?

9. The 1994 Cowboys just missed out on making it a hat-trick of successive Super Bowl appearances, losing 38-28 in the NFC Championship game to which team?

10. The Cowboys claimed their fifth World Championship a year later, defeating which team 27-17 in Super Bowl XXX?

11. Which head coach steered the Cowboys to glory in Super Bowl XXX?

12. Which stadium hosted Super Bowl XXX?

13. Which tight end scored the Cowboys' opening touchdown in Super Bowl XXX?

14. Who was appointed the team's head coach in February 1998?

15. In a 1998 game against the Giants, who became the first Cowboy to score an interception and punt return touchdown in the same game?

16. Which alliteratively named defensive lineman led the team in sacks in 1991, 1993 and 1996?

17. Who was the offensive coordinator on the 1992 and 1993 World Championship-winning teams?

18. Which speedy receiver's 90-yard catch against the 49ers in 1994 is the longest in team history that didn't result in a touchdown?

19. How many losing seasons did the Cowboys record during the 1990s? a) zero b) one c) two

20. How many division titles did the Cowboys win during the 1990s? a) five b) six c) seven

Quiz 15: Answers

1. Quincy Carter 2. Marion Barber 3. Barry Switzer 4. Eight 5. Don Meredith 6. Mike Nolan 7. False 8. Rayfield Wright 9. Roger Staubach 10. False – He suffered just one losing season 11. Detroit 12. Miles Austin 13. Roger Staubach, Tony Dorsett and Herschel Walker 14. Tennessee and UCLA 15. #82 16. Bob Lilly 17. Robert Newhouse 18. Jason Witten 19. a) $140m 20. c) 270

Quiz 17: Pot Luck

1. Which defensive lineman, despite recording double digit sacks in five different seasons between 1983 and 1994, never made it to the Pro Bowl?

2. Which Cowboy is the only player on the losing team to be awarded the Super Bowl MVP award?

3. In 2002, Emmitt Smith became the NFL's all-time leading rusher. Whose record did he break?

4. Who was the first head coach in franchise history who failed to take his team to the playoffs?

5. 'Fear No Evil' and 'All The Rage' are the titles of books by which former Dallas defensive star?

6. The Cowboys' biggest every victory was a 56-7 thrashing of which rival?

7. How many playoff games did the Cowboys lose under Jimmy Johnson's tenure as head coach?

8. Between 1987 and 1991 the Cowboys lost eight straight games to which team?

9. Tony Romo threw his final career touchdown pass to which receiver?

10. True or false – The Cowboys recorded losing seasons in each of Tom Landry's first five years as head coach in Dallas?

11. Which Cowboy was the winner of the 2012 Walter Payton NFL Man of the Year Award?

12. What number jersey did star defensive lineman Randy White wear?

13. The team award which is voted for by Cowboys fans and honors sportsmanship, dedication, leadership and achievement is named after which player?

14. Who famously said 'We will win the ballgame' three days before the 1994 NFC Championship decider?

15. Who caught an acrobatic 45-yard touchdown pass in Super Bowl XII despite suffering a broken thumb earlier in the game?

16. Which former St Louis Rams head coach was appointed the Cowboys' offensive coordinator in 2015?

17. The Cowboys have met every NFC team in the playoffs bar one. Which one?

18. Before taking the reins in Dallas Barry Switzer spent 14 years as head coach of which college team?

19. In 2012, Jason Witten set the NFL record for the most catches by a tight end in a season with how many receptions? a) 109 b) 110 c) 111

20. What is the most points conceded by the Cowboys in a single game? a) 52 b) 53 c) 54

Quiz 16: Answers

1. Buffalo 2. Cowboys 52-17 Bills 3. Troy Aikman 4. The Rose Bowl 5. Jimmie Jones and Ken Norton 6. Buffalo 7. Emmitt Smith 8. James Washington 9. San Francisco 10. Pittsburgh 11. Barry Switzer 12. Sun Devil Stadium 13. Jay Novacek 14. Chan Gailey 15. Deion Sanders 16. Tony Tolbert 17. Norv Turner 18. Alvin Harper 19. c) Two 20. b) Six

Quiz 18: 2000s

1. Who was appointed head coach in January 2000?

2. In December 2000, Emmitt Smith became just the third back in NFL history to rush for 15,000 yards. Who were the first two to reach that milestone?

3. Emmitt Smith was one of two Dallas backs with a 1,000-yard rushing season during the 2000s. Who was the other?

4. Which quarterback, who started nine games for the Cowboys in 2002, also played baseball for the St Louis Cardinals?

5. Who came out of retirement in 2003 to become the team's sixth head coach?

6. Who was the only Cowboys quarterback voted to the Pro Bowl throughout the 2000s?

7. Who were the two Cowboys with over 1,000 receiving yards in a single season during the 2000s?

8. Which linebacker, who led the team in tackles in 2001, 2003 and 2004, was the first Vietnamese-American to play in the NFL?

9. Which quarterback won more games as a starter for the Cowboys – Quincy Carter or Drew Bledsoe?

10. Who led the team in sacks for five straight seasons between 2001 and 2005?

11. Which San Diego defensive coordinator was named the Dallas head coach in 2007?

12. The 2006 Cowboys lost a Wild Card game to which team after Tony Romo fumbled a hold on the potential winning field goal?

13. How many times did the Cowboys reach the NFC Championship game in the 2000s?

14. Which wide receiver returned punts for touchdowns in back-to-back games against Atlanta and Seattle in 2009?

15. Which kicker scored rushing touchdowns in both 2000 and 2001?

16. The Cowboys lost 33-24 to which AFC North team in the last game hosted at Texas Stadium?

17. Who caught a 60-yard pass in overtime to give the Cowboys a 26-20 win over the Chiefs in October 2009?

18. Reggie Swinton was the only Cowboy to do what throughout the whole of the 2000s?

19. How many division titles did the Cowboys win throughout the decade? a) none b) one c) two

20. What was the most games won by the Cowboys during a single regular season during the 2000s? a) 11 b) 12 c) 13

Quiz 17: Answers

1. Jim Jeffcoat 2. Chuck Howley 3. Walter Payton 4. Dave Campo 5. Charles Haley 6. Philadelphia 7. One 8. Philadelphia 9. Terrance Williams 10. True 11. Jason Witten 12. #54 13. Bob Lilly 14. Jimmy Johnson 15. Butch Johnson 16. Scott Linehan 17. New Orleans 18. Oklahoma 19. b) 110 receptions 20. c) 54

Quiz 19: Pot Luck

1. What is the most games that the Cowboys have won in a single regular season?

2. The Bounty Bowl was the nickname given to two brutal 1989 games between the Cowboys and which team?

3. 'The Hotel' was the nickname of which dominant offensive lineman?

4. Toby Gowin, Sam Paulescu and Mike Saxon have all played which position for the Cowboys?

5. Who is the only Cowboys head coach to have an overall losing win loss percentage?

6. Which Dallas head coach was the author of a book called 'Turning the Thing Around: My Life in Football'?

7. How many turnovers did the Cowboys force in Super Bowl XXVII?

8. In October 2011, the Cowboys blew a franchise record 23-point lead while losing 34-30 to which NFC Central team?

9. True or false – The Cowboys reached the playoffs every year during the 1970s?

10. Which 2021 NFL head coach was the defensive coordinator in Dallas from 2000 through to 2006?

11. Which linebacker won NFC Player of the Month honors in both 2011 and 2013?

12. Who are the two Dallas kickers to have converted over 100 field goals?

13. True or false – Chan Gailey had a better regular season winning percentage with the Cowboys than Jimmy Johnson?

14. Did Tony Romo score more or fewer than 10 rushing touchdowns throughout his entire career with the Cowboys?

15. Which Heisman Trophy-winning running back spent the final year of his NFL career with the Cowboys in 2004?

16. Former head coach Jason Garrett appeared for which four NFL teams during his quarterback playing career?

17. 'Dandy Don' was the nickname of which former Cowboy?

18. What is the most sacks that the Cowboys have given up in a single game?

19. In 2008, the Cowboys set an NFL record after how many players made it to the Pro Bowl? a) 11 b) 12 c) 13

20. Which team did the Cowboys face in their first ever NFL game? a) Chicago b) Green Bay c) Pittsburgh

Quiz 18: Answers

1. Dave Campo 2. Walter Payton and Barry Sanders 3. Julius Jones 4. Chad Hutchinson 5. Bill Parcells 6. Tony Romo 7. Jason Witten and Terrell Owens 8. Dat Nguyen 9. Quincy Carter 10. Greg Ellis 11. Wade Phillips 12. Seattle 13. None 14. Patrick Crayton 15. Tim Seder 16. Baltimore 17. Miles Austin 18. Return a kickoff for a touchdown 19. c) Two 20. c) 13

Quiz 20: 2010s

1. Which head coach was fired eight games into the 2010 season?

2. The Cowboys had the same win-loss record in each of Jason Garrett's first three full seasons as Dallas head coach. What was it?

3. The Cowboys played their first ever game on a Wednesday in the 2012 season opener, defeating which defending Super Bowl champion 27-14?

4. Which colorful character was the team's defensive coordinator in 2011 and 2012?

5. Whose first NFL touchdown was a 91-yard scamper against the Rams in October 2011?

6. The Cowboys claimed their 22nd Division title in 2014 after routing which AFC South team by a score of 42-7?

7. True or false – The 2014 Cowboys were the first team in franchise history to go unbeaten in road games?

8. In September 2014, the Cowboys overturned a franchise record 21-point deficit to defeat which team?

9. The 2014 Cowboys were eliminated from the playoffs following a controversial 26-21 loss to which team?

10. Which receiver's seemingly good 'catch' was ruled incomplete in the closing stages of that playoff loss?

11. The 2016 Cowboys tied a franchise record after winning how many regular season games?

12. The Cowboys exited the playoffs in the Divisional round, losing 34-31 to which team?

13. The 2015 Cowboys suffered their worst season in over 20 years. How many games did they win?

14. Which former Washington back rushed for 547 yards at an average of 4.8 yards per carry during the 2017 season?

15. In 2016, the Cowboys set a team recorded for the fewest interceptions in a season. How many passes did they pick off?

16. Who returned punts for 78 and 86-yard touchdowns in 2012 and 2013?

17. In 2013, who became the first Cowboys defensive tackle since Randy White to record double-digit sacks in a season?

18. The 2016 Cowboys tied a franchise record after winning how many consecutive regular season games?

19. The 2014 Cowboys scored the second highest number of points in a single season in team history with how many? a) 457 b) 467 c) 477

20. Which offensive lineman was not selected in the first round of the NFL Draft? a) La'el Collins b) Travis Frederick c) Zack Martin

Quiz 19: Answers

1. 13 games 2. Philadelphia 3. Flozell Adams 4. Punter 5. Dave Campo 6. Jimmy Johnson 7. Nine 8. Detroit 9. False – they missed out once 10. Mike Zimmer 11. Sean Lee 12. Rafael Septien and Dan Bailey 13. True 14. Fewer than 10 15. Eddie George 16. Dallas, New York Giants, Tampa Bay and Miami 17. Don Meredith 18. 11 sacks 19. c) 13 20. c) Pittsburgh

Quiz 21: Pot Luck

1. What is the highest number of losses suffered by the Cowboys in a single season?

2. Did the Cowboys have an overall winning or losing record in games played at Texas Stadium?

3. Which team did the Cowboys face in Jimmy Johnson's last game as Dallas head coach?

4. Which former Cowboy was the winner of season three of the TV talent show 'Dancing With The Stars'?

5. Who won more regular season games as Dallas head coach – Barry Switzer or Wade Phillips?

6. 'Bullet' was the nickname of which speedy Cowboys receiver?

7. True or false – Emmitt Smith was the first player in NFL history to rush for over 1,000 yards in 11 successive seasons?

8. Do the Cowboys have a winning or losing record in games against Philadelphia?

9. Which backup quarterback threw a 50-yard 'Hail Mary' to Drew Pearson on Thanksgiving Day 1974 to give the Cowboys a memorable 24-23 win over Washington?

10. Deion Sanders wore what number jersey?

11. In a 1985 game the Cowboys defense sacked which Houston quarterback a franchise record 12 times?

12. Which controversial visiting receiver almost caused a riot after celebrating a touchdown by dancing on the Cowboys star?

13. True or false – On Christmas Day 2000 the Cowboys fumbled a franchise record eight times?

14. Who was the owner of the Cowboys before Jerry Jones?

15. Which Dallas defender was named the NFC Defensive Player of the Year in 1994?

16. Who caught and ran for a 53-yard gain against the Eagles in 2007 despite having his helmet ripped off?

17. Which offensive lineman prevented what looked like a certain pick six, tackling linebacker Darion Conner in a 1994 game against the Saints?

18. Tom Landry famously wore what style of hat?

19. The hottest ever game to feature the Cowboys was against the Eagles in 2000 when temperatures got how high? a) 107F b) 108F c) 109F

20. The Cowboys recorded their first NFL regular season victory against which team? a) Cleveland b) Minnesota c) Pittsburgh

Quiz 20: Answers

1. Wade Phillips 2. 8 wins 8 losses 3. New York Giants 4. Rob Ryan 5. DeMarco Murray 6. Indianapolis 7. True 8. Arizona 9. Green Bay 10. Dez Bryant 11. 13 games 12. Green Bay 13. Four 14. Alfred Morris 15. Six 16. Dwayne Harris 17. Jason Hatcher 18. 11 games 19. b) 467 20. a) La'el Collins

Quiz 22: Numbers Game

Identify the jersey number worn by the following Cowboys players.

1. Tony Romo and Rodney Peete

2. Michael Irvin and Dez Bryant

3. Ezekiel Elliott and Julius Jones

4. Danny White and Cole Beasley

5. Charles Haley and DeMarcus Ware

6. Marion Barber and Everson Walls

7. Terrell Owens and Rocket Ismail

8. Darren Woodson and Felix Jones

9. Rafael Septien and Mat McBriar

10. Emmitt Smith and Bob Hayes

11. Jim Jeffcoat and Tyron Smith

12. DeMarco Murray and Kenneth Gant

13. Brandon Weedon and Jon Kitna

14. Don Meredith and Quincy Carter

15. Doug Free and Herb Scott

16. Charlie Waters and Terence Newman

17. Mike Ditka and Gavin Escobar

18. Mel Renfro and Darren McFadden

19. La'Roi Glover and Jason Hatcher

20. Doug Cosbie and Jay Novacek

Quiz 21: Answers

1. 15 games 2. Winning 3. Buffalo 4. Emmitt Smith 5. Barry Switzer 6. Bob Hayes 7. True 8. Winning 9. Clint Longley 10. #21 11. Warren Moon 12. Terrell Owens 13. True 14. Bum Bright 15. Charles Haley 16. Jason Witten 17. Larry Allen 18. A fedora 19. c) 109F 20. c) Pittsburgh

Quiz 23: Pot Luck

1. Do the Cowboys have a winning or losing record in games against the New York Giants?

2. In what year did the Cowboys play their first game at AT&T Stadium?

3. Which divisional foe defeated the Cowboys in the first game at AT&T Stadium?

4. Who does the play-by-play commentary on Cowboys radio broadcasts?

5. Which former quarterback is the color analyst on Cowboys radio broadcasts?

6. During their first four seasons what color helmets did the Cowboys wear?

7. Which 1970s era safety was nicknamed 'Captain Crash'?

8. Do the Cowboys have a winning or losing record in Monday Night Football games?

9. True or false – During the 1976 season the Cowboys' helmet featured red, white and blue stripes?

10. Which 38-year-old quarterback threw 16 touchdown passes en route to a 4-5 starting record with the Cowboys in 2010?

11. Who was the Dallas offensive coordinator during Wade Phillips' tenure as head coach?

12. Which team won the first Super Bowl hosted at AT&T Stadium?

13. 'Power Money and Sex: How Success Almost Ruined My Life' was a book by which former Dallas star?

14. Which quarterback was suspended and then traded to the Chargers after sucker-punching Roger Staubach?

15. In what year did the Cowboys record the 500th win in team history (including playoff games)?

16. What number jersey did full back Daryl Johnston wear?

17. Which four quarterbacks started games for the Cowboys during the 2014 season?

18. Between 1974 and 1979 the Cowboys won nine consecutive games against which opponent?

19. Michael Irvin's career was cut short after he suffered an injury to what part of his body? a) ankle b) knee c) spine

20. What is the highest number of interceptions recorded by the Cowboys in a single season? a) 35 b) 36 c) 37

Quiz 22: Answers

1. #9 2. #88 3. #21 4. #11 5. #94 6. #24 7. #81 8. #28 9. #1 10. #22 11. #77 12. #29 13. #3 14. #17 15. #68 16. #41 17. #89 18. #20 19. #97 20. #84

Quiz 24: Anagrams

Rearrange the letters to make the name of a current or former Cowboys player or coach.

1. Tracked Post

2. Okay Martin

3. Try Almond

4. Two Tin Jeans

5. Not Roomy

6. Him Nice Rival

7. Dotty Tenors

8. Treats Jargon

9. Hardy Twine

10. Learn Rally

11. Android Sense

12. Eco Eyeballs

13. Beady Nail

14. Curb A Shortage

15. Warmer Sauced

16. Yes Reach Hall

17. Barrio Barmen

18. Poor America

19. Slim Aunties

20. Unscrewed Caramel

Quiz 23: Answers

1. Winning 2. 2009 3. New York Giants 4. Brad Sham 5. Babe Laufenberg
6. White 7. Cliff Harris 8. Winning 9. True 10. Jon Kitna 11. Jason Garrett
12. Green Bay 13. Deion Sanders 14. Clint Longley 15. 2014 16. #48 17.
Tony Romo, Matt Cassel, Brandon Weedon and Kellen Moore 18.
Philadelphia 19. c) Spine 20. c) 37

Quiz 25: Pot Luck

1. 'The Playmaker' was the nickname of which Dallas offensive star?

2. Who are the two Cowboys to have recorded three interceptions in the Super Bowl?

3. Before Ezekiel Elliott in 2016, who was the last Dallas first-round draft pick whose first name and surname started with the same letter? (clue: it was a defensive lineman)

4. Which Hall of Fame defensive back arrived in Dallas as a highly rated running back?

5. 'Shoot For The Star' was the title of which long-serving Dallas defender's autobiography?

6. True or false – Texas Stadium once played host to the Pro Bowl?

7. A 2000 contest against Cincinnati was the last time the Cowboys didn't do what in a game?

8. Jason Garrett started his NFL coaching career as quarterbacks coach with which AFC team?

9. True or false – The Cowboys have never won a game played on Christmas Day?

10. Do the Cowboys have a winning or losing record in overtime games?

11. What do the initials L.P. stand for in the name of long snapper L.P. Ladouceur?

12. What was AT&T Stadium known as before the naming rights deal was agreed?

13. True or false – The Cowboys had only 10 men on the field during Tony Dorsett's historic 99-yard touchdown run in 1983?

14. Which Dallas head coach coined the phrase 'How 'bout them Cowboys'?

15. The Cowboys scored 20 fourth quarter points to secure a 30-27 win over which team in the Divisional Round of the 1980 playoffs?

16. Which Dallas defensive back blocked four punts in two games in the 1970s?

17. What was the name of the song and video recorded by the Cowboys team during the mid-1980s?

18. Who is the only player in team history to play under five different head coaches?

19. Dak Prescott holds the NFL record for the most passes without an interception to start his career. How many did he throw without a pick? a) 156 b) 166 c) 176

20. Who was the previous holder of that record? a) Tom Brady b) John Elway c) Dan Marino

Quiz 24: Answers

1. Dak Prescott 2. Troy Aikman 3. Tom Landry 4. Jason Witten 5. Tony Romo 6. Michael Irvin 7. Tony Dorsett 8. Jason Garrett 9. Randy White 10. Larry Allen 11. Deion Sanders 12. Cole Beasley 13. Dan Bailey 14. Roger Staubach 15. DeMarcus Ware 16. Charles Haley 17. Marion Barber 18. Amari Cooper 19. Miles Austin 20. DeMarcus Lawrence

Bonus Questions

Bonus Questions: Quiz 1

1. In 2019, the Cowboys sent a first round draft pick to which team to acquire the services of Amari Cooper?

2. Which team have the Cowboys defeated the most times in postseason games?

3. The longest postseason pass in team history was a 94-yard touchdown from Troy Aikman to which receiver in the 1994 Divisional Round Playoff game against the Packers?

4. Which Cowboys head coach was elected to the Pro Football Hall of Fame as part of the class of 2020?

5. In March 2021, who signed a contract that made him the highest paid player in franchise history?

6. Which Cowboys pass rusher returned a fumble 98 yards for a score in an October 1999 game against Arizona?

7. If all the Cowboys' head coaches were listed alphabetically by surname, who would be first on the list?

8. After Tom Landry, who has spent the most seasons as the head coach of the Cowboys?

9. Which pair of Cowboys receivers topped the 1,000-yard mark in 2019?

10. What number jersey does receiver Amari Cooper wear?

11. Who was the last non-kicker to lead the team in single season scoring? (Clue: It was in 2006)

12. Which Cowboy holds the record for the most NFL appearances by a Canadian?

13. How many games did the Cowboys win in Mike McCarthy's first season as head coach?

14. True or false – A team from the Cowboys once appeared on the TV gameshow 'Family Feud'?

15. True or false – AT&T Stadium has hosted the NFL Draft?

16. Which Dallas defensive back scored his first career touchdown with a pick six of Philadelphia quarterback Jalen Hurts in September 2021?

17. In which round of the 2019 NFL Draft did the Cowboys select running back Tony Pollard?

18. Who is the only Cowboy to score more than 100 points in six different seasons?

19. How many quarterbacks were picked ahead of Dak Prescott in the 2016 NFL Draft? a) 6 b) 7 c) 8

20. What is Dak Prescott's given first name? a) Ralph b) Raymond c) Rayne

Bonus Quiz 5 Answers

1. Dez Bryant 2. Zack Martin 3. DeMarco Murray and Darren McFadden 4. Emmitt Smith 5. Ed Jones 6. Atlanta, Chicago and Tampa Bay 7. D.D. Lewis 8. Troy Aikman 9. Seattle 10. Jimmy Johnson 11. Dak Prescott 12. Leighton Vander Esch 13. Nick 14. True 15. Micah Parsons 16. Dez Bryant 17. #88 18. Garrett Gilbert 19. c) Roger Staubach 20. c) 17

Bonus Questions: Quiz 2

1. Who is the only defender to have started more than 200 games for the Cowboys?

2. Which opponent from the AFC have the Cowboys beaten the most times?

3. Who returned a punt 83 yards for a touchdown in a November 2017 game against Washington?

4. The Cowboys overturned a 20-point deficit before going on to beat which opponent 40-39 in September 2020?

5. In a January 2007 game against the Seahawks, who became the first Cowboy to return a kickoff for a touchdown in a playoff game?

6. True or false – According to Forbes Magazine, the Dallas Cowboys is the most valuable franchise in the NFL?

7. Defensive star Micah Parsons played college ball at which school?

8. In 2020 who became just the fourth tight end in team history to catch 60 or more passes in a single season?

9. Which former quarterback was named the Cowboys' offensive coordinator in 2019?

10. Before Amari Cooper, who was the last Dallas receiver to top 90 catches in a season?

11. Who returned an Eli Manning interception a franchise record 101 yards for a touchdown in a November 2010 game against the Giants?

12. Up to the start of the 2021 season, only one NFC team had registered more postseason wins than the Cowboys. Which one?

13. Who holds the franchise record for the most Pro Bowl appearances by a Cowboys tackle?

14. Who was the offensive coordinator on the 1995 World Championship-winning team?

15. True or false – Dak Prescott has never thrown double digit interceptions in a single season?

16. Was Troy Aikman's longest career run more or less than 20 yards?

17. Excluding Tom Landry, which Cowboys head coach has the most postseason wins?

18. What is the name of the official Cowboys magazine?

19. Up to the start of the 2021 season, the Cowboys had suffered more playoff defeats at the hands of which team than any other? a) 49ers b) Packers c) Rams

20. What does the C in the name of Dallas defender C.J. Goodwin stand for? a) Charaun b) Chavez c) Chazeem

Bonus Quiz 1 Answers

1. Oakland 2. San Francisco 3. Alvin Harper 4. Jimmy Johnson 5. Dak Prescott 6. Greg Ellis 7. Dave Campo 8. Jason Garrett 9. Amari Cooper and Michael Gallup 10. #19 11. Marion Barber 12. L.P. Ladouceur 13. Six 14. True 15. True 16. Trevon Diggs 17. Fourth 18. Dan Bailey 19. b) 7 QBs 20. c) Rayne

Bonus Questions: Quiz 3

1. Do the Cowboys have an overall winning or losing record in playoff games?

2. Which Cowboys safety, who appeared in five Super Bowls, was elected to the Pro Football Hall of Fame in 2020?

3. Who are the two Cowboys running backs to have led the NFL in rushing in two of their first three seasons in the league?

4. Dak Prescott registered a career-best 502 passing yards in an October 2020 game against which AFC North opponent?

5. In November 2014, the Cowboys played their first regular season game in London, defeating which opponent 31-17?

6. Which famous venue hosted that historic London game?

7. Defensive star Micah Parsons wears what number jersey?

8. Who holds the franchise record for the most receptions by a Cowboys rookie?

9. Jaylon Smith and Zack Martin both played college ball at which school?

10. Who was the last Cowboy to register more than 10 sacks in back-to-back seasons?

11. If all the Cowboys' head coaches were listed alphabetically by surname, who would be last on the list?

12. Do the Cowboys have a winning or losing record in games that have gone to overtime?

13. Who caught 11 passes for a career best 226 yards in an October 2019 game against the Packers?

14. Which defensive back intercepted five passes in the first four games of the 2021 season?

15. If all the players to have appeared for the Cowboys throughout their history were listed alphabetically, who would be last on the list?

16. In a December 1973 game against the Vikings, Golden Richards became the first, and so far only, Cowboy to do what in a playoff game?

17. True or false – The Cowboys failed to win a single playoff game during Jason Garrett's tenure as head coach?

18. Which quarterback, who spent two seasons in Dallas in 2004 and 2005, had previously played professional baseball for the New York Yankees?

19. Including postseason play, the Cowboys longest winning streak stretched to how many games? a) 11 b) 12 c) 13

20. Between 2003 and 2017, Jason Witten set a franchise record after starting how many consecutive games? a) 169 b) 179 c) 189

Bonus Quiz 2 Answers

1. Ed Jones 2. Pittsburgh 3. Ryan Switzer 4. Atlanta 5. Miles Austin 6. True 7. Penn State 8. Dalton Schultz 9. Kellen Moore 10. Dez Bryant 11. Bryan McCann 12. Green Bay 13. Tyron Smith 14. Ernie Zampese 15. False 16. More 17. Jimmy Johnson 18. Star 19. c) Rams 20. a) Charaun

Bonus Questions: Quiz 4

1. Of Cowboys quarterbacks with at least 1,500 attempts, who has the lowest interception percentage?

2. In December 1966, the Cowboys registered their first postseason victory. Which now AFC team did they defeat by a score of 52-14?

3. Which Dallas linebacker registered at least 150 tackles in 2018, 2019 and 2020?

4. Who was the last Cowboys defender before him to register three successive 150-tackle seasons?

5. Who is the Cowboys' all-time leading rusher in playoff games?

6. Former Cowboys quarterback Tony Romo has gone on to become a successful broadcaster. Who is his usual partner in the commentary booth?

7. Which Cowboys offensive star was inducted in the Pro Football Hall of Fame as part of the Class of 2021?

8. True or false – Dallas defensive back Trevon Diggs is the brother of the Bills receiver Stefon Diggs?

9. Before joining the Cowboys, Mike McCarthy won a Super Bowl ring as the head coach of which team?

10. Which executive, who was Director of Player Personnel for the Cowboys between 1960 and 1988 was inducted into the Pro Football Hall of Fame in 2019?

11. Who did the Cowboys select with the 12th overall pick of the 2021 NFL Draft?

12. Who are the three Cowboys to have won the NFL Man of the Year Award? (Clue: They were in 1978, 1997 and 2012).

13. Which wide receiver threw his first career touchdown pass in a 37-34 win over the Giants in October 2020?

14. Who was the unlikely receiver of that touchdown pass?

15. Which 2021 NFL head coach spent three seasons with the Cowboys as a tight end from 2003 until 2005?

16. Which quarterback threw 14 touchdown passes and had a 4-5 record as a starter in his only season in Dallas in 2020?

17. Who scored rushing, receiving and kickoff return touchdowns in his rookie season in 2020?

18. Which team did the Cowboys face in the game known as 'The Ice Bowl'?

19. The 2019 Cowboys offense set a franchise record after amassing how many yards? a) 6,704 yards b) 6,804 yards c) 6,904 yards

20. What was CeeDee Lamb's given first name? a) Cadavius b) Cedarian c) Codeel

Bonus Quiz 3 Answers

1. Winning 2. Cliff Harris 3. Emmitt Smith and Ezekiel Elliott 4. Cleveland 5. Jacksonville 6. Wembley Stadium 7. #11 8. CeeDee Lamb 9. Notre Dame 10. DeMarcus Lawrence 11. Barry Switzer 12. Winning 13. Amari Cooper 14. Trevon Diggs 15. Greg Zuerlein 16. Return a punt for a TD 17. False 18. Drew Henson 19. b) 12 games 20. c) 179 games

Bonus Questions: Quiz 5

1. Dak Prescott threw his first career touchdown pass to which receiver?

2. Which Cowboys lineman was the only offensive rookie to receive Pro Bowl recognition in 2014?

3. In 2014 and 2015, for the first time in team history the Cowboys had different rushers pass the 1,000-yard barrier in successive seasons. Who were the two backs?

4. Who holds the team record for scoring the most points in a single season with 150?

5. Whose 19 opposition fumble recoveries between 1974 and 1989 are the most in franchise history?

6. Up to the start of the 2021 season, the Cowboys had a 100% winning record in playoff games against which three NFC opponents?

7. Which long serving linebacker appeared in a franchise record 27 playoff games between 1968 and 1981?

8. Who is the only Dallas quarterback to have thrown for more than 350 yards in a single playoff game?

9. Dan Quinn won a Super Bowl as the defensive coordinator of which team?

10. Which former Cowboys head coach appeared on the reality TV series 'Survivor'?

11. Who is the only Cowboy who is not a running back to have been named the AP NFL Offensive Rookie of the Year?

12. Whose 176 tackles in 2018 are the most in team history by a Cowboys rookie?

13. What is the name of Zack Martin's brother who was drafted by the Texans in 2016 before moving to the Raiders?

14. True or false – AT&T Stadium has hosted the NCAA Men's Basketball Final Four?

15. 'Harmonic Pass' is an anagram of the name of which 2021 Cowboys star?

16. Before CeeDee Lamb in 2020, who was the last wide receiver to be picked by the Cowboys in the first round of the NFL Draft?

17. What number jersey does receiver CeeDee Lamb wear?

18. Which backup quarterback threw his first career touchdown pass (to CeeDee Lamb) in a November 2020 loss to the Steelers?

19. Who holds the record for the most rushing yards by a Cowboys quarterback? a) Dak Prescott b) Tony Romo c) Roger Staubach

20. In the 1991 NFL Draft the Cowboys set a franchise record after drafting how many players? a) 15 b) 16 c) 17

Bonus Quiz 4 Answers

1. Dak Prescott 2. Cleveland 3. Jaylon Smith 4. Bradie James 5. Emmitt Smith 6. Jim Nantz 7. Drew Pearson 8. True 9. Green Bay 10. Gil Brandt 11. Micah Parsons 12. Roger Staubach, Troy Aikman and Jason Witten 13. Cedrick Wilson 14. Dak Prescott 15. Dan Campbell 16. Andy Dalton 17. CeeDee Lamb 18. Green Bay 19. c) 6,904 yards 20. b) Cedarian

Made in United States
North Haven, CT
17 December 2022

29440144R00039